Mystery Mob
and the
Bonfire Night Plot

Roger Hurn

Illustrated by
Stik

RISING ★ STARS

Rising Stars UK Ltd.
22 Grafton Street, London W1S 4EX
www.risingstars-uk.com

The right of Roger Hurn to be identified as the author of this work
has been asserted by him in accordance with the Copyright,
Design and Patents Act 1988.

Published 2008

Text, design and layout © Rising Stars UK Ltd.

Cover design: Burville-Riley Partnership
Illustrator: Stik, Bill Greenhead for Illustration Ltd
Text design and typesetting: Andy Wilson
Publisher: Gill Budgell
Editor: Catherine Baker

British Library Cataloguing in Publication Data.
A CIP record for this book is available from the British Library

ISBN: 978-1-84680-424-3

Printed in the UK by CPI Bookmarque, Croydon, CR0 4TD

Mixed Sources
Product group from well-managed
forests and other controlled sources
www.fsc.org Cert no. TT-COC-002227
© 1996 Forest Stewardship Council
FSC

Contents

Meet the Mystery Mob

Name:

Gummy

FYI: Gummy hasn't got much brain – and even fewer teeth.

Loves: Soup.

Hates: Toffee chews.

Fact: The brightest thing about him is his shirt.

Name:

Lee

FYI: If Lee was any cooler he'd be a cucumber.

Loves: Hip-hop.

Hates: Hopscotch.

Fact: He has his own designer label (which he peeled off a tin).

Name:

Rob

FYI: Rob lives in his own world – he's just visiting planet Earth.

Loves: Daydreaming.

Hates: Nightmares.

Fact: Rob always does his homework – he just forgets to write it down.

Name:

Dwayne

FYI: Dwayne is smarter than a tree full of owls.

Loves: Anything complicated.

Hates: Join-the-dots books.

Fact: If he was any brighter you could use him as a floodlight at football matches.

Name:

Chet

FYI: Chet is as brave as a lion with steel jaws.

Loves: Having adventures.

Hates: Knitting.

Fact: He's as tough as the chicken his granny cooks for his tea.

Name:

Adi

FYI: Adi is as happy as a football fan with tickets to the big match.

Loves: Telling jokes.

Hates: Moaning minnies.

Fact: He knows more jokes than a jumbo joke book.

What a Guy!

The Mystery Mob's home town
has a huge firework display on
5th November. Last year it beat
a nearby town, Little Wallop, to win
the title of Best Bonfire Night Show.
Everyone in the town wants to beat
Little Wallop and win the title again
this year.

Dwayne, Gummy, Chet and Adi are helping to build the big bonfire, while Rob and Lee are making the guy.

Rob   Okay, so we've got the lifelike Guy Fawkes mask, but what do we do next?

Lee   That's easy. We stuff some old clothes with newspaper to make the body.

Rob   Okay.
I've got loads
of old trousers
and stuff. I'll go and get them.

Lee   No way! You've got terrible
taste in clothes. I'm not having
the guy dressed in your castoffs.
This guy has got to look good!

Rob   Huh? It's going on the bonfire,
Lee – not the London Fashion
Show.

Lee   So what? Our guy is going to be
the best guy ever.

Rob Well, I guess we'd better use your old clothes then.

Lee You must be joking. I don't have any old clothes. I only wear the latest designer gear.

Rob Duh! They'd be no good anyway.

Lee Why not?

Rob 'Cos Guy Fawkes lived in the olden days.

Lee So?

Rob So his clothes have got to be well out of date. And where are we going to find clothes like that?

Lee I've got it! Your dad's suit is really old fashioned and so is that big floppy hat your mum always wears. They're just what we need for our guy.

Rob Wicked! Let's go and get them.

Rob and Lee make their guy with
Rob's dad's suit and his mum's hat.
It looks fantastic. Everybody is really
impressed. They are just about to put
the guy on top of the bonfire when
two angry people come running up.

Rob's dad Oi! What do you two think
you're doing? Give me back
my suit! It's my best one!

Rob's mum
How dare you, Robbie?
That's my favourite hat.

Rob's mum and dad take their clothes
back. They're so cross they take
the Guy Fawkes mask too. Not only that,
but they tell Rob that if he tries making
a guy with their stuff again, he'll be
grounded!

Now the town doesn't have a guy
for its bonfire. Everyone is cross
with Rob and Lee. The organisers
tell them to get another guy in time
for Bonfire Night – or else!

A Guy from Nowhere

It's the day of the big firework display. Rob and Lee still haven't had any luck getting hold of another guy.

Lee   I can't believe your mum and dad. Anyone would think they *want* Little Wallop to beat us.

Rob   Yeah, without a guy we haven't got a hope.

Lee   That's not true. Our fireworks
        are the best. So we'll still win.

Rob   Hmmm … maybe, but I don't
        want to be us when we have to
        tell everyone we haven't got
        a guy.

Lee looks out of the window.

Lee   We won't have to, Rob.
        Look, someone's left a guy
        here in my front garden.

Rob   I wonder who did that?

Lee   I don't know, but there's a note
pinned to the guy's hat.

The boys go out and take a closer look
at the guy. The note says, 'Guys,
I've made you a guy. Good luck!
Hope you win.'

Rob   Wow! How kind. Who wrote
the note?

Lee   I haven't got a clue. It just says
it's from a well-wisher.

Rob   Cool.

Lee   Yeah. Anyway, now we've got
a guy, we're out of trouble.
This guy is so good it almost
looks real. Come on, Rob,
let's take him down to the bonfire.

Rob   Okay. Hey, this guy's heavy.
He needs to go on a diet.
I can't lift him.

Lee   No worries. Let's put Guy in my
dad's wheelbarrow and then
we can wheel him to the bonfire.

Rob   But I thought it was Catherine who got wheeled, not Guy.

Lee   Doh!

Everyone is really impressed with Rob and Lee's guy. They all say how lifelike it is. Rob and Lee forget to mention that they didn't actually make it.

Lee   Right, Rob. Let's put this guy up on top of the bonfire.

Rob   How are we going to do that?

Lee   We just loop this rope under his arms, and then we get the rest of the Mystery Mob to help us pull him up.

Rob   Great idea. Let's do it.

The boys pull the guy up to the top of the bonfire.

Rob   Wow! The guy looks great up there.

Lee   Little Wallop doesn't have a chance of winning the title now.

A Ghostly Guy

Lee and Rob take the wheelbarrow back to Lee's house. Rob looks puzzled.

Rob   Can I ask you something?

Lee   Sure. What is it?

Rob   Can dummies speak?

Lee   Yeah, a dummy like Gummy never shuts up.

Rob   No, I mean a dummy like our Guy Fawkes dummy.

Lee   Of course not.

Rob   Only I'm sure I heard it say 'ouch' when we pulled it up the bonfire.

Lee   Trust me, Rob. A stuffed dummy can't speak.

Rob   So, if a stuffed dummy can't speak, what have we put on top of the bonfire? 'Cos it definitely said 'ouch'.

Lee   Hmmm … that's a good
question. I think we'd better go
back and check that dummy out.

Rob and Lee hurry back to the bonfire.
There is no one else about.

Rob   Where's everybody gone?

Lee   They've all gone home for
their tea. They'll be back as soon
as it gets dark. That's when
DJ Beatbox is going to start
the show by lighting the bonfire.

Rob   Cool.

Lee   Yeah, if you can call
a raging fire cool.

Rob   Then our guy will go up
in flames.

Lee   That's right. What a horrible
way to go.

Rob   (terrified) Oh no, Lee.
I think the guy agrees with you.
Look! It's come to life.

Rob points to the top of the bonfire.
The dummy is standing up.

Lee   Oh – this is soooo creepy.

Rob   (gulping) Maybe the dummy
is haunted by the ghost
of Guy Fawkes.

Lee   Yeah, and it's climbing down
from the bonfire 'cos it doesn't
want to be a toasty ghosty.

Rob   You got it!

Lee   Duh! I don't think so.
            That dummy is way too heavy
            to be a ghost.

Rob   So what is it?

Lee   Don't ask me. I'm as much
            in the dark as you are.

Rob   But we're not in the dark.
            If we were, DJ Beatbox would
            be here and the fireworks
            would have started.

Lee   Rob, when they were giving out brains you were definitely at the back of the queue.

Rob   Huh! Well, at least I'm not the one who thinks we're in the dark.

Lee   (sighing) Whatever.

Rob   Arghhhh! The guy has almost reached the ground.

Lee   Quick, let's hide behind
this fire engine.

Rob   Right! Then we can spy on him
and see what he's up to.

The boys duck behind a fire engine
that is parked by the bonfire. It's there
in case anything goes wrong
at the firework display.

A Sneaky Guy

The guy creeps over to the Park Keeper's shed. It's locked, so he takes a skeleton key from his pocket.

Lee Hmmm ... that's sneaky.
He's got a skeleton key.

Rob A skeleton key! Oh no,
that proves our guy's a ghost.

Lee No, it proves he's a bad guy
up to no good. A ghost could
just walk through the wall.

Rob   Well, whatever he is,
he's breaking into the shed.
But why is he doing that?

Lee   That's where all the fireworks
for tonight's display are kept.

Rob   Yes, but what does Guy Fawkes
want with fireworks?

Lee   I don't know, but I think
we're about to find out.

The guy comes out of the shed with
a large box of fireworks in his arms.
He staggers over to the bonfire with it.

Rob   Hey, he's putting all the fireworks on the bonfire.

Lee   He's trying to ruin our town's firework display.

Rob   We've got to do something.

Lee   You're right. Let's find the organisers. They can put a stop to this.

Rob   I think it's too late for that, Lee.

Lee   Why?

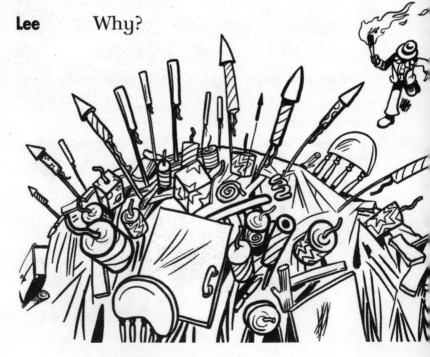

Rob   'Cos now he's got a burning torch and he's going to use it to set the bonfire alight!

Lee   Okay, Rob, it's down to you and me to save the town's firework display before he ruins it.

Rob   Right! But I've only got one thing to say to that.

Lee   Which is?

Rob   How?

A Jealous Guy

Rob and Lee stand there scratching their heads.

Lee   Wait a minute. We're a couple of dummies. What are we hiding behind?

Rob   It's this big, red shiny thing.

Lee   Yes, it's called a fire engine.

Rob   I know that.

Lee   And fire engines have hosepipes.

Rob   Gotcha!

Lee   So let's roll out the hosepipe
and blast Guy with a jet
of cold water before he can
set the bonfire alight.

Rob and Lee grab hold of the hosepipe.
Guy is nearly at the bonfire. He holds
the burning torch above his head.
He is just about to throw it on to
the dry wood. Rob and Lee take
careful aim.

Rob   Let him have it, Lee.

Lee   Here goes!

The force of the jet knocks the flaming
torch out of Guy's hand. It goes out
with a splutter. Now Lee and Rob turn
the hosepipe on to Guy. They drench him
with freezing water.

Guy   Arrrrgh! Stop it.
         You're soaking me!

Rob   We'll stop it when you tell us
         who you are.

Lee   You're not Guy Fawkes.

Rob   You're not even a guy
         called Fawkes.

Guy   Grrrr! No, I'm the man who runs
the Little Wallop firework show.
I knew your Bonfire Night
display would beat ours
so I thought up a plot to ruin it.
Now please turn that hose off.

Lee   Okay, but you've got to put
all the fireworks back
and then tell everyone
what you tried to do.

Guy   No way.

Rob   Shall we turn the water
back on, Lee?

Lee   You bet!

Guy   All right, you win. I'll confess.
I can't take any more
of that freezing watcr!

DJ Beatbox and the organisers arrive.
The man from Little Wallop admits
what he's done. Then he goes off
sneezing. All that icy water has given him
a cold.

Rob   Huh, that Guy Fawkes bloke turned out to be a damp squib, didn't he?

Lee   That's true, but his Bonfire Night plot certainly went right up in smoke!

The Bonfire Night Show is a big success and the town wins the title again – thanks to Rob and Lee.

About the author

Roger Hurn has:

- had a hit record in Turkey
- won *The Weakest Link* on TV
- swum with sharks on the Great Barrier Reef.

Now he's a writer, and he hopes you like reading about the Mystery Mob as much as he likes writing about them.

Bonfire Night quiz

Questions

1 Who tried to blow up Parliament in 1605?
Was it:

   A Some guy called Fawkes
   B Guy Fawkes
   C Knives and Forks

2 What do you get if you cross a dinosaur with fireworks?

3 What do you call a good-looking Guy Fawkes dummy?

4 What did the Catherine Wheel say to her friends?

5 What kind of firework do angry teachers give to naughty children?

6 What kind of firework can you eat with mashed potatoes?

7 What firework never stays in one place?

8 What do you call a firework that goes out in the rain?

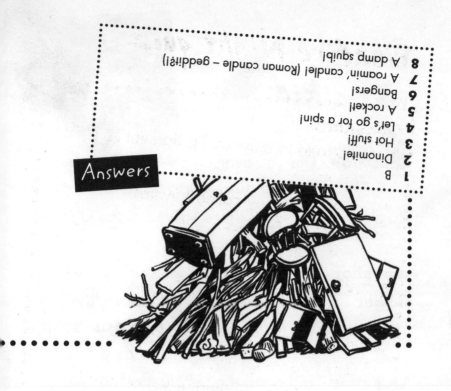

Answers

1 B
2 Dinomite!
3 Hot stuff!
4 Let's go for a spin!
5 A rocket!
6 Bangers!
7 A roamin' candle! (Roman candle – geddit?!)
8 A damp squib!

How did you score?

- If you got all eight Bonfire Night answers correct, then you're too hot to handle!

- If you got six Bonfire Night answers correct, then you're a really bright spark!

- If you got fewer than four Bonfire Night answers correct, then you should definitely retire *before* lighting the blue touch paper!

When I was a kid

Question Did you ever make a guy when you were a kid?

Roger Yes. And that's how I got the idea for this Mystery Mob story.

Question What do you mean?

Roger Well, back in those days we used to put the guy in a pram and ask people to give us 'a penny for the guy'.

Question Did people give you much money?

Roger No, nobody gave me anything because my guy was rubbish. So then I had a brilliant idea.

Question What was it?

Roger I dressed my little sister up like a guy and put her in the pram.

Question Did you get more money then?

Roger No, my little sister spoiled it by yelling for our mum. She thought I was trying to sell her for a penny!

Adi's favourite Bonfire Night joke

What do you call a dummy who has steel prongs instead of hands?

Guy Forks!

How to have fun and stay safe on Bonfire Night

✸ Always go to a public firework display. Don't try to have a firework party in your back garden. They can be very dangerous – especially when your mum finds out how much your dad has spent on buying the fireworks.

✸ *Don't dress up as Guy Fawkes – you might end up on the bonfire!*

✸ All fireworks are dangerous so never play with them or try to light them.

✸ *Be a bright spark and wear gloves if you are going to hold a sparkler. Never run around with a sparkler in your hand.*

✹ When your sparkler has gone out, put it in a bucket of water. They stay hot for ages, unlike your Bonfire Night hot dog!

✹ *You may love Bonfire Night, but pets don't like fireworks. So don't take your pet with you when you go to watch a display – let it stay safe and warm at home. Anyway, why would you want to take a goldfish to a firework party?*

Five fantastic facts about Bonfire Night

1 Guy Fawkes tried to blow up the King and the Houses of Parliament on the 5th November 1605. His plot failed and he was arrested. People celebrated by lighting bonfires in the streets.

2 Bonfires used to be called 'bone fires' – yuck!

3 People only started making 'Guys' to burn on their bonfires in 1806, 200 years after the plot. Poor Guy!

4 There is a rhyme about Guy Fawkes' plot which we still chant today. It goes like this:

   'Remember, remember the fifth of November
   The gunpowder, treason and plot,
   I know of no reason why gunpowder treason
   Should ever be forgot.'

5 In the old days, children used to make guys and then ask people to give them 'a penny for the guy'. They used the money to buy fireworks!

Bonfire Night lingo

Blue touch paper The fuse on a firework. Once it's been lit by an adult – stand well back!

Damp squib A firework that fails to go off. A damp squid is a creature that lives in the ocean.

Guy A dummy that children make to burn on the bonfire. Not another word for bloke.

Guy Fawkes Punch Don't worry, this isn't Guy Fawkes trying to knock you out cold. In fact, it's a hot spicy drink that warms you up on bonfire night.

Parkin A sticky ginger cake that people in Yorkshire eat at Bonfire Night parties. It's not what you do when you leave your car somewhere.

Penny for the Guy Children used to ask for 'a penny for the guy' when showing off their homemade guys. These days you can't buy much for a penny – and you certainly shouldn't buy fireworks!

Mystery Mob

Mystery Mob Set 1:

Mystery Mob and the Abominable Snowman
Mystery Mob and the Big Match
Mystery Mob and the Circus of Doom
Mystery Mob and the Creepy Castle
Mystery Mob and the Haunted Attic
Mystery Mob and the Hidden Treasure
Mystery Mob and the Magic Bottle
Mystery Mob and the Missing Millions
Mystery Mob and the Monster on the Moor
Mystery Mob and the Mummy's Curse
Mystery Mob and the Time Machine
Mystery Mob and the UFO

Mystery Mob Set 2:

Mystery Mob and the Ghost Town
Mystery Mob and the Bonfire Night Plot
Mystery Mob and the April Fools' Day Joker
Mystery Mob and the Great Pancake Day Race
Mystery Mob and the Scary Santa
Mystery Mob and the Conker Conspiracy
Mystery Mob and the Top Talent Contest
Mystery Mob and the Night in the Waxworks
Mystery Mob and the Runaway Train
Mystery Mob and the Wrong Robot
Mystery Mob and the Day of the Dinosaurs
Mystery Mob and the Man-eating Tiger

RISING ★ STARS

Mystery Mob books are available from most booksellers.

**For mail order information
please call Rising Stars on 0871 47 23 010
or visit www.risingstars-uk.com**